Author's Note

I am an ESOL tutor based in Leeds. I was inspired by the Gatehouse Books I used with my students to write some beginner reading material of my own, using my own photographs and text. I designed them in comic book style, to appeal to a wider audience, and aimed the text at the Entry level 1 and 2 ESOL learner.

The *Liz and Joe* series is very popular with my students, who enjoy following the same characters, seeing different aspects of their lives and comparing everyday situations with their own.

It is exciting and rewarding to have them published by Gatehouse Books.

Jennie Cole

It was Sunday morning and there was a knock at the door.

It was one of Liz and Joe's neighbours.

Liz opened the door.

The woman looked very worried.

8

Liz and Joe listened to their neighbour.

Get Talking!

You and your pets

Do you have any pets?

What would you do if your pet went missing?

How could you help your neighbour if their pet was missing?

Gatehouse Books®

Gatehouse Books are written for older teenagers and adults who are developing their basic reading and writing or English language skills.

The format of our books is clear and uncluttered. The language is familiar and the text is often line-broken, so that each line ends at a natural pause.

Gatehouse Books are widely used within Adult Basic Education throughout the English speaking world. They are also a valuable resource within the Prison Education Service and Probation Services, Social Services and secondary schools - both in basic skills and ESOL teaching.

Catalogue available

Gatehouse Media Limited
PO Box 965
Warrington
WA4 9DE

Tel: 01925 267778
E-mail: info@gatehousebooks.com
Website: www.gatehousebooks.com